BATMAN

GOTHAM SHALL BE JUDGED

BATMAN

GOTHAM SHALL BE JUDGED

David Hine

Fabian Nicieza

Peter Calloway

Writers

Cliff Richards

Guillem March

Freddie Williams II

Andres Guinaldo

Lorenzo Ruggiero

Walden Wong

Tomeu Morey

Guillem March

Guy Major

JD Smith

Colorists

Sal Cipriano

John J. Hill

Dave Sharpe

Jared K. Fletcher

Carlos M. Mangual

Rachel Gluckstern Mike Marts Editors – Original Series
Janelle Asselin Harvey Richards Associate Editors – Original Series
Rickey Purdin Katie Kubert Assistant Editors – Original Series
Robin Wildman Editor
Robbin Brosterman Design Director – Books

Eddie Berganza Executive Editor
Bob Harras VP – Editor-in-Chief

Diane Nelson President
Dan DiDio and **Jim Lee** Co-Publishers
Geoff Johns Chief Creative Officer
John Rood Executive VP – Sales, Marketing and Business Development
Amy Genkins Senior VP – Business and Legal Affairs
Nairi Gardiner Senior VP – Finance
Jeff Boison VP – Publishing Operations
Mark Chiarello VP – Art Direction and Design
John Cunningham VP – Marketing
Terri Cunningham VP – Talent Relations and Services
Alison Gill Senior VP – Manufacturing and Operations
David Hyde VP – Publicity
Hank Kanalz Senior VP – Digital
Jay Kogan VP – Business and Legal Affairs, Publishing
Jack Mahan VP – Business Affairs, Talent
Nick Napolitano VP – Manufacturing Administration
Sue Pohja VP – Book Sales
Courtney Simmons Senior VP – Publicity
Bob Wayne Senior VP – Sales

BATMAN: GOTHAM SHALL BE JUDGED

DC Comics, 1700 Broadway, New York, NY 10019
A Warner Bros. Entertainment Company.
Printed by RR Donnelley, Salem, VA, USA. 3/2/12. First Printing.
ISBN: 978-1-4012-3378-5

SUSTAINABLE
FORESTRY
INITIATIVE
Certified Chain of Custody
At Least 25% Certified Forest Content
www.sfiprogram.org
SFI-01042
APPLIES TO TEXT STOCK ONLY

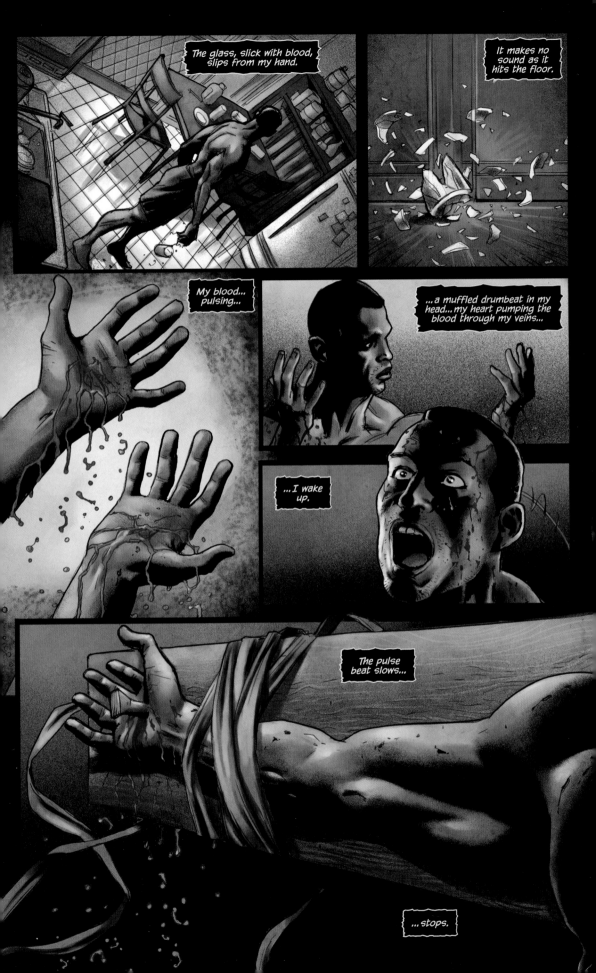

A CENTURIES-OLD RELIGIOUS CULT IN SEARCH OF A SAVIOR. A HAUNTED ARMOR. SWORDS THAT WIELD ALCHEMICAL FIRE AND ICE. AN EX-COP IN NEED OF SALVATION. MICHAEL LANE IS ONE CRUSADER FOREVER LINKED TO BATMAN'S DESTINY... HE IS...

AZRAEL

Three Mysteries
PART ONE: A DREAM WITHIN A DREAM

WRITER · DAVID HINE   ARTIST · CLIFF RICHARDS
COLORS · TOMEU MOREY   LETTERING · SAL CIPRIANO
EDITOR · RACHEL GLUCKSTERN   COVER · GUILLEM MARCH
AZRAEL CREATED BY DENNY O'NEIL AND JOE QUESADA

THE BATCAVE.

...AND THEN THERE'S THE PROBLEM OF *AZRAEL*.

...KNEW *THAT* WAS COMING.

BRUCE WAYNE
BATMAN

DICK GRAYSON
BATMAN

I HAD A DREAM, DICK. A VISION OF THREE GHOST BATMEN.

THE THIRD BATMAN SOLD HIS SOUL TO THE *DEVIL* AND DESTROYED GOTHAM.

AND THE THIRD MAN WAS *MICHAEL LANE*, RIGHT?

I MADE THE DECISION TO LET HIM KEEP THE *AZRAEL* ARMOR, BRUCE. SEEMED TO ME HE GOT A BUM DEAL ALL ROUND.

DESERVED A CHANCE TO MAKE GOOD.

AND HOW'S THAT GOING?

NOT GOOD. HE ISN'T A BIG FAN OF DUE PROCESS. HE PREFERS TO HAND DOWN HIS OWN PUNISHMENT.

THERE ARE TIMES WHEN THAT AMOUNTS TO THE DEATH PENALTY WITH NO APPEAL TO A HIGHER COURT.

YOU ARE TROUBLED.

I KNOW YOU WANTED THE SUIT FOR YOURSELF, BUT THIS IS HOW IT MUST BE.

WHY *HIM?* WHY *MICHAEL LANE?*

HE'LL TURN AGAINST US.

MICHAEL LANE WAS *DESTINED* TO WEAR *THE SUIT OF SORROWS* SINCE THE DAY HE WAS BORN.

GRIEVE THOUGHT HE WAS THE ONLY ONE WHO KNEW THAT.

THE ORDER HAS NO SECRETS FROM *RA'S AL GHUL...*

...AND I HAVE NO SECRETS FROM *YOU,* MY FAITHFUL FRIEND.

CONSOLE YOURSELF WITH THIS THOUGHT.

IF HE *FAILS* TO LIVE UP TO HIS DESTINY, I PROMISE YOU, THE SUIT WILL BE *YOURS.*

FADI NASER
THE WHITE GHOST

Three Mysteries

PART TWO: VOICES IN AN EMPTY ROOM

WRITER · DAVID HINE   ARTIST · CLIFF RICHARDS
COLORS · TOMEU MOREY   LETTERING · JOHN J. HILL
EDITOR · RACHEL GLUCKSTERN   COVER · GUILLEM MARCH
AZRAEL CREATED BY DENNY O'NEIL AND JOE QUESADA

...SOMEONE WHO WANTS TO ELIMINATE MY FAMILY'S BLOODLINE.

WHY WOULD ANYONE--?

I CAN'T TELL YOU. YOU WOULDN'T BELIEVE ME.

TRY ME.

WHAT *DID* HE TELL YOU?

IT'S A SECRET.

JENNY, HE *KILLED HIMSELF!* I NEED TO KNOW WHY.

YOU'LL FIND OUT WHY, WHEN THE TIME'S RIGHT.

DON'T BE SO IMPATIENT.

Is insanity catching? First Michael Lane, then Farelli, now Jenny.

HE'S SPECIAL, YOU KNOW. *REALLY* SPECIAL.

THAT'S WHAT I KEEP HEARING.

What else happened last night? What did he do to you?

I ALWAYS KNEW HE WASN'T *RIGHT*. SURE, ALL YOU PEOPLE GOT YOUR QUIRKS, BUT AZRAEL...?

YOU ASK ME, HE WAS ALWAYS PART OF THE *PROBLEM*.

GOTHAM POLICE HEADQUARTERS.

IS FORENSICS DONE WITH THE SUIT?

The suit is the key to all this.

I'LL NEED MY OWN SAMPLES.

HELP YOURSELF. YOU WILL ANYWAY, RIGHT? LET YOURSELF OUT WHEN YOU'RE DONE.

UH-HUH. PRELIMINARY REPORT SAYS THE MATERIALS HAVE BEEN INFUSED WITH AN "UNKNOWN CHEMICAL COMPOUND."

Talia wanted the Suit of Sorrows for Damian. She said it would help him fulfill his destiny.

But *what* destiny?

POISON TONGUE

Three Mysteries

PART THREE: FIRE THE COLOR OF ICE

WRITER · DAVID HINE   ARTIST · CLIFF RICHARDS

COLORS · TOMEU MOREY   LETTERING · SAL CIPRIANO

EDITOR · RACHEL GLUCKSTERN   COVER · GUILLEM MARCH

AZRAEL CREATED BY DENNY O'NEIL AND JOE QUESADA

I've been watching Ra's al Ghul's safe house for more than two days.

DICK GRAYSON
BATMAN

ANY MOVEMENT?

BRUCE WAYNE
BATMAN

THE GUARDS ARE PATROLLING THE PERIMETER AS USUAL.

THE HOUSE IS SHUT DOWN TIGHT. NO ONE IN OR OUT.

BRUCE, THERE'S SOMETHING I NEED TO ASK YOU.

OF COURSE. YOU CAN *ALWAYS* TALK TO ME.

RIGHT. SO... I WANT TO KNOW HOW WE GOT HERE. YOU SAID YOU FOLLOWED AZRAEL'S *SUIT OF SORROWS*.

HOW?

THERE WAS NO TRACKING DEVICE. IT DOESN'T LEAVE A RADIOACTIVE TRAIL.

I WORE THE SUIT. EVERYONE WHO HAS IS LINKED WITH IT.

BAGHDAD.
MARCH 2003.

It used to bug the hell out of my cousin, when I played my guitar.

<DEGENERATE WESTERN TRASH.>

It also bugged him that I spoke in English. He understands English as well as me, but he refuses to speak it.

WHEN THE AMERICANS COME, I'M STARTING A BAND. THEY'LL NEED ENTERTAINMENT.

HOW ABOUT IT? YOU WANT TO SING IN MY BAND?

<IF THE AMERICANS COME, I WILL *FIGHT* THEM.>

HAKIM, YOU'RE MY FAVORITE COUSIN AND I LOVE YOU, BUT YOU ARE A *JERK.*

When the bombs fell, I played to drown out the noise.

I closed my eyes and turned up the volume...

THERE IS A PLACE KNOWN AS *THE CAVE OF TEARS.*

WHEN THE WIND RISES FROM THE EAST, IT CLEARS THE SAND TO REVEAL A SHEET OF GLASS AROUND THE CAVE.

THIS IS HOW THE PLAIN OF GLASS CAME TO BE...

The Tears Of God
PART TWO OF TWO: FIRE AND SAND

WRITER · DAVID HINE   ARTIST · CLIFF RICHARDS
COLORS · TOMEU MOREY   LETTERING · DAVE SHARPE
ASSISTANT EDITOR · RICKEY PURDIN   EDITOR · RACHEL GLUCKSTERN
COVER · GUILLEM MARCH
AZRAEL CREATED BY
DENNY O'NEIL AND JOE QUESADA

MICHAEL WASHINGTON LANE. *AZRAEL.*

SAMI MOUSAWI *FIREBALL,* ALSO KNOWN AS AZRAE

TO AZRAEL, IT FELT AS IF THE SUN ITSELF HAD TUMBLED FROM THE SKY AND ENGULFED HIM IN ITS RAGING HEAT.

THE VERY SAND AROUND HIM MELTED.

WHAT USE IS MY POWER? I NEVER SAVED ANYONE.

YOU'RE AN ANGEL OF *DEATH*, SAMI. YOU WERE NEVER MEANT TO SAVE LIVES.

COME. THERE'S NOTHING LEFT FOR YOU HERE.

WHY DIDN'T YOU TELL ME THE TRUTH? THERE WAS NO REASON FOR ME TO FIGHT FIREBALL.

WHAT IF I HAD *KILLED* HIM?

THEN HE WOULD NOT HAVE BEEN THE ONE. HE HAD TO BE TESTED, JUST AS YOU WERE.

SAMI!

...UNNGHH...

HAKIM...HE'S BURNING... I LEFT HIM TO BURN...

THE FLIGHT HOME WAS LONG. *RA'S al GHUL,* THE DEMON'S HEAD, USED THE TIME TO TELL HIS ANGELS OF DEATH THE PLANS HE HAD LAID FOR THEM. PLANS THAT HAVE WAITED CENTURIES TO COME TO FRUITION.

HIS WORDS WERE SWEET POISON IN THEIR EARS.

PRACTICE. NATURAL ABILITY...

...AND YOU ARE VERY, *VERY* SLOW.

Save the lives of a couple of cops... take one more perp off the streets...

A routine night.

TAKE ME DOWN WITH WHAT?

HOW DID YOU--?

OKAY, BATMAN. WE'LL TAKE IT FROM HERE.

NO! THIS ISN'T *FAIR!* I HAD THEM *DEAD TO RIGHTS!*

He really needs to chill.

YOU'VE BUILT UP A REAL HEAD OF STEAM THERE, EDDIE.

IF YOU WANT TO BLOW OFF SOME OF THAT AGGRESSION, WHY NOT TAKE A PUNCH AT ME?

DO YOU THINK THAT'S A GOOD IDEA, SIR?

GO AHEAD. GIVE IT YOUR BEST SHOT.

Alfred is such a worrywart.

NOT SO *SPECIAL* NOW, ARE YOU?

THE GIRLS WON'T BE CHASING YOU AROUND MUCH FROM HERE ON, YA LITTLE *FREAK!*

The memories aren't real.

This never happened.

DICK... PLEASE...

...MASTER DICK...

MASTER DICK!

IT'S OKAY, ALFRED. I TOOK A NAP.

I'M ON MY WAY HOME.

Okay, there's no denying it. The bruise has changed shape.

It *feels* like a bruise, but I guess it's technically an entry wound.

Entry wound, exit wound. But the X-rays were clear. No internal trauma.

ANY CHANCE OF BREAKFAST?

NONE AT ALL. IT'S FIVE-THIRTY, *POST* MERIDIEM.

HEY, ALL THE BEST DINERS SERVE BREAKFAST ALL DAY.

MY KITCHEN IS *NOT* A DINER.

ARE YOU SURE YOU'RE WELL?

PERHAPS I SHOULD GIVE YOU A SCAN?

DID ONE MYSELF A COUPLE OF DAYS BACK.

I'M JUST TIRED. THIS *IS* A HIGH-STRESS OCCUPATION, YOU KNOW.

THAT BUILDING... THERE COULD BE PEOPLE--

--WAY AHEAD OF YOU.

YES, GO ON. BE AN *ANGEL*.

AND TAKE CARE...

"...DON'T FALL."

NO! TANYA!

WAAAAAHH

MY BABY'S IN THERE!

GO! I'LL TAKE CARE OF YOUR BABY!

It will be far worse the next time. This is just a *taste* of what they can do.

WHAT HAPPENED? WHERE ARE THEY?

MY EYES! I CAN'T SEE A THING!

I can feel the wound on my chest...the skin crawling like it's alive...I did this... I brought this to Gotham...

I can. It takes more than a few fireworks to take out my sensors. Azrael and the Crusader are gone.

WHAT WAS *THAT* ALL ABOUT?

I THOUGHT AZRAEL WAS SANCTIONED BY YOU-KNOW-WHO.

NOT EXACTLY. WE'RE AWARE THAT HIS STATE OF MIND IS FRAGILE.

YEAH, WELL I'D SAY IT'S TIME FOR HIS MEDICATION.

SERIOUSLY, YOU SHOULD BE CALLING IN THE BIG GUNS HERE, BECAUSE THE TWO OF YOU DIDN'T EVEN COME CLOSE TO TAKING DOWN THE CRUSADER, LET ALONE AZRAEL.

NOT YET. HE GAVE US TWENTY-FOUR HOURS.

WHY WAIT? WHY ALLOW *THEM* TO SET THE AGENDA?

AZRAEL IS *MY* RESPONSIBILITY. IF THINGS GET OUT OF HAND, WE'LL GET HELP.

Be honest, Grayson. The truth is I *need* to deal with this without the help of Bruce or anyone else.

MOVE ALONG, PEOPLE. NOTHING TO SEE HERE.

I need to pass Azrael's test.

I need to know that I am a *good* person.

"MY *ANGELS OF DEATH* WILL PUT THE HEROES OF GOTHAM TO THE TEST..."

"...AND WHEN THEY FAIL THAT TEST..."

"...GOTHAM WILL *BURN*."

My **Mom** was a little religious, my **Dad** not at all.

So when she was **killed**-- and my Dad was left in a **coma**--I didn't have a strong foundation of **faith** to turn to.

By the time my **father** was killed-- then so many of my friends--all I had left to turn to was **anger**.

It was **easier** than believing in a God who had let that happen.

But anger solved little and when the world was in **crisis**--

--I prayed.

I heard only **silence**.

So I confessed my sins...and realized I had **none**.

How could someone who tried so hard to be good--did so much for so many people--be asked to endure so much?

He calls himself the *Crusader.* Telekinetic. Pyrokinetic. Maybe telepathic. **Definitely** insane.

Rapture crazy.

He came to support *Azrael*--a former cop, former insane Batman and current Soldier of God named **Michael Lane**--

--who may or may not be of direct divine descent. Yes, I said that.

They decided to go Sodom and Gomorrah on Gotham City.

The only hope to spare their "wrath" was if one of three people-- *Batman, Catwoman* or *myself*--

--would be judged worthy in their eyes.

I'm being "tested" now. Azrael is holding Mayor Hady hostage--

--but *Dick Grayson* is Gotham's Batman and he has to call the shots.

STATUS UPDATE.

NO CHANGE. THEY HAVEN'T COME AFTER ME OR *CATWOMAN*. THEY'RE STANDING BY WHAT THEY SAID--TESTING US ONE AT A TIME, *RED ROBIN.*

ALL THE MORE REASON WE SHOULD BE HITTING THE *ORDER OF PURITY* AND LANE'S *FAMILY*--

NO. NOT YET. UNTIL WE LEARN MORE ABOUT THIS CRUSADER--

--AND IF THERE IS AN ULTIMATE PLAY BEYOND JUST RELIGIOUS FANATICISM--

--WE KEEP THINGS UNDER CONTROL BY LETTING THEM THINK THEY'RE IN CONTROL.

WHICH SHOULD BE DOABLE SINCE THEY *ARE.*

The question is... why...?

Why is Dick letting them set the agenda...?

WHAT'S CATWOMAN DOING?

ASKED HER TO LIE LOW AND WAIT.

WHAT ARE THE ODDS OF *THAT*?

Selina Kyle doesn't like having her strings pulled.

She's doing what I *should* be--*tangling* those strings--

--finding out how to tie Lane into knots the way he's tying *us*--

--what *secrets* is he hiding--family--friends--family...?

I let Dick handle the new Azrael from the beginning.

That was a *mistake*, because now I don't have enough intel.

GCPD

VOICE COMMAND TO TEXT: CALL *MONEY-SPIDER*.

LONNIE, I NEED SOME HELP.

MATTERS. OF. FAITH. TROUBLING. YOU.

GOTHAM COMMUNITY CLINIC

Red Robin: Lonnie, I need some help.
MoneySpider: Matters of faith troubling

Lonnie Machin is my info-jock, mired in body, wired in mind.

YOU ARE MY *WHITE GHOST* BECAUSE OF YOUR FAITH IN ME.

I FOUND THAT FAITH A TESTAMENT OF YOUR WORTHINESS TO SERVE.

BUT BECAUSE MEASURES OF FAITH ARE SO... *SUBJECTIVE*-- AND *FLAWED*--

--THE CITY'S CHAMPIONS HAVE LOST THEIR *BEST* CHANCE TO SAVE GOTHAM.

THE *MORAL FAILINGS* OF BOTH GRAYSON AND KYLE--

--WILL *MAKE* THEIR TESTS A MOOT POINT IN THESE PROCEEDINGS...

AND BECAUSE OUR *ANGELS OF DEATH* SEEK SOMETHING THAT SIMPLY DOES NOT EXIST...

"...GOTHAM CITY DIES AT *DAWN*..."

Well, you got your-self into quite a mess. Even for you.

You leave Ivy to deal with Harley breaking into Arkham to kill Joker--

--just so you could see what was going on at Devil's Square.

And now, here you are, with two super-powered psychopaths threatening to destroy Gotham unless you pass their test.

Except you don't know where they are, what the test is, or even if the test is going to happen.

That's a great way to get yourself killed...

...damn my curiosity.

CATWOMAN.

SO, RED ROBIN FAILED, HUH?

HOW'D YOU KNOW?

BECAUSE YOU'RE CALLING ME.

...

He thinks I'm going to fail.

GET READY. YOUR TEST IS NEXT--AZRAEL AND CRUSADER WILL BE COMING FOR YOU.

Would now be a bad time to tell him I don't do well with tests?

COMING FOR ME?

HONEY... IN CASE YOU HAVEN'T NOTICED--

--I'M NOT THE KINDA GIRL WHO WAITS AROUND.

MICHAEL LANE'S BROWNSTONE.

Disturbing this window will set off the silent alarm.

I could work around it. It'd be an easy thing to do. Child's play.

But what's the fun in *that?*

KRASH

And unlike most times I break into a house, this time I *want* the attention.

Okay, this is getting annoying. Where **are** you, you psycho son of a--

DON'T DO IT.

THAT'S ALL THE WARNING YOU'RE GONNA GET.

JENNY LANE

WIDOW OF MICHAEL LANE'S LATE BROTHER.

CRAACK

I TOLD YOU NOT TO DO IT.

YOU BROKE INTO MY HOME! WHAT AM I SUPPOSED TO DO?

YOU MUST BE JENNY.

HOW'D YOU-- YOU KNOW WHAT, I DON'T EVEN CARE. JUST TAKE WHAT-EVER YOU WANT AND GO.

I'M NOT HERE TO STEAL FROM YOU. IF I WAS, YOU NEVER WOULD'VE KNOWN I WAS HERE. I'M HERE FOR MICHAEL, YOUR BROTHER-IN-LAW.

HE'S GONE CRAZY.

SAYS THE LADY WHO BROKE INTO MY HOUSE DRESSED IN A SKINTIGHT CAT COSTUME.

MICHAEL'S GOING TO DESTROY GOTHAM UNLESS I PASS A TEST.

OKAY, FIRST I GET SOME CRAZY PRANK CALL SAYING MICHAEL IS GOING TO DESTROY GOTHAM, THEN YOU START SPOUTING THE SAME CRAZY NONSENSE.

FUNNY. AND WHAT WOULD YOU SAY IS THE COMMON DENOMINATOR?

MICHAEL WOULD NEVER DESTROY GOTHAM.

CRRRR RRRRRIIIIIIPPPPP

NO? WELL, YOU KNOW EVERYTHING THAT'S GOING ON AT DEVIL'S SQUARE AND THE MAYOR'S MANSION?

SELINA KYLE. YOUR JUDGMENT IS NEAR. WILL YOU CHOOSE TO CLEANSE YOUR SOUL?

CLEANSE MY SOUL?

YOU GOT A COUPLE OF YEARS?

BECAUSE IN CASE YOU HAVEN'T NOTICED--

--THERE ISN'T ONE OF THE TEN COMMANDMENTS I *HAVEN'T* BROKEN.

ME NEITHER.

BUT I AM NOT INTERESTED IN THE TEN COMMANDMENTS.

IT DOES YOU NO GOOD TO ATONE FOR BREAKING COMMANDMENTS YOU HAVE NO WISH TO HEED.

I WANT YOU TO ATONE FOR JUST *ONE SIN.*

THE ONE *YOU* HAVE NEVER FORGIVEN YOUR-SELF FOR.

SELINA KYLE'S TEST IS OVER. SHE DID NOT SUCCEED.

YOU SOUND SURPRISED.

"SHE AND HER SISTER HAVEN'T HAD THE MOST...FRIENDLY OF RELATIONSHIPS."

MAGGIE, COME HOME. WE CAN--

NO.

I DON'T WANT TO BE ENEMIES--

GOODBYE, DEMON.

"BUT THE BONDS OF FAMILY RUN DEEP."

SISTER MAGDALENE. WILL YOU JOIN US?

PERHAPS. BUT NOT TONIGHT.

TIMOTHY DRAKE. SELINA KYLE. BOTH HAVE FAILED.

NOW THERE'S JUST ONE THING STANDING BETWEEN OUR PLANS AND GOTHAM'S DESTRUCTION...

...DICK GRAYSON.

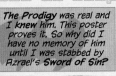

SO YOU'LL KILL US ALL TO TEACH THE WORLD A LESSON IN HUMILITY.

DOES THAT INCLUDE JENNY AND HER KIDS?

NO. I'LL NEVER HARM THEM.

THEY'RE ALREADY ON THEIR WAY OUT OF THE CITY.

LOOKS LIKE THEY MADE A WRONG TURN.

YOU THINK THIS IS THE RIGHT THING TO DO? IF THOSE KIDS GET HURT--

IF I'M WRONG, *EVERYBODY* DIES, CATWOMAN.

BRING THEM UP HERE.

WHY ARE YOU HERE, JENNY? PARATINO HAD ORDERS TO TAKE YOU TO SAFETY.

ADRIAN PARATINO IS AT THIS MOMENT DESPERATELY TRYING TO BREAK DOWN THE CELLAR DOOR WITH HIS BARE HANDS.

MAYBE HE'LL MAKE IT BEFORE DAWN. MAYBE NOT. IT'S A WELL-BUILT DOOR.

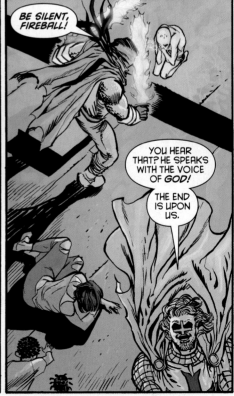

UNNNGHH!

MY SWORDS... PLEASE, LET ME HAVE THEM.

WHAT'S WRONG? WHAT DID YOU SEE?

IT'S NOT *GOD'S* WILL TO DESTROY GOTHAM.

IT'S *RA'S AL GHUL* WHO WANTS IT. HE'S *USING* ME.

GOD HELP ME. WHAT DO I DO?

HOW DO I STOP THIS?

IT'S OUT OF YOUR HANDS, MASTER.

FIREBALL IS LOSING CONTROL!

The city trembles and quakes.

Every window within a half-mile radius shatters.

But Gotham stands.

Miraculously, there has only been one casualty here.

IS IT OVER?

TIM DRAKE
RED ROBIN

SELINA KYLE
CATWOMAN

WHAT ARE YOU TWO DOING HERE? I THOUGHT I MADE IT CLEAR YOU SHOULD STAY AWAY.

JUST AS WELL WE DIDN'T. YOU FAILED YOUR TEST, JUST LIKE WE DID. IF WE HADN'T BROUGHT JENNY...

YOU ALL PASSED YOUR TESTS. YOU ARE RIGHTEOUS AND WORTHY HEROES.

IT IS I WHO FAILED.

I LISTENED TO THE SERPENT'S LIES. I DID SATAN'S WORK HERE.

CRUSADER, TAKE US AWAY FROM HERE.

WAIT! I CAN'T LET YOU LEAVE.

YOU CAN'T STOP ME.

MICHAEL!